MY NEW MASK

**Written and Illustrated by Christa Lawrence
to benefit Mundelein Parks Foundation**

MI NUEVA MASCARA

A story brought to you by
Mundelein Park & Recreation District

Este libro
incluye el
en español.

Today my mom told me that I would need to wear a mask when we went out. I thought I would look like this:

But she told me that wasn't the kind of mask I need to wear. I need to wear a mask that will protect me from getting sick. At first it felt strange, but I am getting used to it.

Mommy said that she and Daddy will wear one too when they go out.

I asked her if my baby brother, Ben would wear a mask. Mommy said he was too little.

My dog Sophie does not need to wear one either. That is good because I don't think she would leave it on.

I do not need to wear a mask when I talk to Grandma and Grandpa on the computer.

Mommy said there were other things we need to do to keep ourselves and others healthy. She said we need to stay six feet apart from other people.

But we don't have to stay far apart from our family.

Daddy says we need to wash our hands a lot. We wash our hands when we come in from outside and after we use the bathroom. I sing Happy Birthday to my toys two times while I wash my hands.

I miss my friends, but Mommy says that when the virus is gone we can play with each other again.

Yesterday I talked to my friend Mia. She told me she was going to dress up as a princess for Halloween.

Can you guess what I told her I was going to be?

MI NUEVA MASCARA

Hoy, mi mama me dijo que necesito
ponerme una mascara para salir.
Yo pensé que me vería así:

Pero ella me dijo que esa no era el tipo de mascara que necesito ponerme. Necesito ponerme una mascara que me protegerá para que no me enferme. Al principio me sentí rara, pero ya me estoy acostumbrando.

Mi mama y mi papa también se pondrán una cundo salgamos.

Le pregunte a mama si mi hermanito, ben, tendría que ponerse una mascara. Ella me dijo que el esta muy chiquito.

Mi perrita sophie no se tiene que poner una mascara tampoco. Que bueno porque no creo que le hubiera gustado y se la quitaría.

No necesito ponerme una mascara cuando hablo con mis abuelitos en la computadora.

Mama me dijo que hay otras cosas que necesitamos hacer para mantenernos sanos y mantener a otros sanos también. Ella me dijo que necesitamos mantener una distancia de seis pies de otra gente.

Pero no tenemos que mantener esa distancia cuando estamos con nuestra familia.

Papa dice que tenemos que lavarnos las manos muchas veces. Tenemos que lavarnos las manos cuando llegamos a la casa y después de ir al baño. Yo le canto "feliz cumpleaños" a mis juguetes dos veces cuando me estoy lavando las manos.

Extraño mucho a mis amigas, pero mi mama dice que cuando el virus sea contenido, podre jugar con mis amigas otra vez.

Ayer hable con mi amiga mia. Ella me dijo que se iba a disfrazar de princesa para halloween.

¿Puedes adivinar que fue lo que le dije
de que me iba a disfrazar?

All proceeds from the sale of this book will benefit

MUNDELEIN PARKS FOUNDATION

Mundelein Parks Foundation... Because all kids should play.

The Mundelein Parks Foundation is a nonprofit charitable organization governed by an independent voluntary board. It was formed in 2005 as staff became aware of an increased need for program scholarships for the residents of Mundelein.

The Mundelein Parks foundation seeks to strengthen community and family ties with a self-generating funding source to finance recreational scholarships to the disadvantaged of the Mundelein community. The recreational scholarships will help furnish hard-working, financially limited residents with the same recreational and leisure opportunities as their neighbors. Monies are raised through tax deductible donations and special events.

To learn more about Mundelein Parks Foundation and Mundelein Park & Recreation District visit mundeleinparks.org

MUNDELEIN PARK & RECREATION DISTRICT
Connecting Our Community

1401 N. Midlothian Rd., Mundelein, IL | 847.566.0650 | mundeleinparks.org

Made in the USA
Columbia, SC
30 September 2020